Universal Edition

EASY JAZZY PIANO

MIKE CORNICK

www.universaledition.com
vienna · london · new york

UE 16 550
ISMN M-008-04278-2
UPC 8-03452-02030-1
ISBN 3-7024-2470-9

EASY JAZZY SERIES

The JAZZY SERIES was written to provide players of moderate abilities with experience of the syncopated patterns of jazz.

Now, the EASY JAZZIES offer this opportunity to players at an earlier stage of their musical development and provide a perfect stepping–stone to the abundance of solo and duet material in the main series.

JAZZY SERIES soll Musikern mit beschränkten technischen Fertigkeiten die Gelegenheit geben, sich mit den synkopierten Rhythmen des Jazz vertraut zu machen.

Mit dem Band EASY JAZZIES bietet sich diese Gelegenheit jungen Musikern nun bereits zu einem früheren Zeitpunkt ihrer musikalischen Entwicklung. Die Stücke stellen ein ideales „Sprungbrett" für das reichhaltige Solo- und Duomaterial der Hauptserie dar.

EASY JAZZY PIANO *by* MIKE CORNICK

This set of piano pieces has been written to provide less experienced pianists with an introduction to a range of jazz–related piano styles. The set includes a ragtime piece and a bossa–nova notated in even quavers and a blues, a ballad, a two–part invention and a jazz waltz which are notated in swing quavers.

The use of swing quavers is indicated by the direction: $\sqcap\!\sqcap = \overset{\ulcorner 3 \urcorner}{\ \rfloor\ \rfloor}$

and this applies to all quaver movement in those pieces, including rests. It may be helpful to rehearse these rhythms before playing the pieces.

Die vorliegende Auswahl an Stücken für Klavier wurde komponiert, um Pianisten mit wenig Erfahrung mit einer Reihe von Einsatzmöglichkeiten des Klaviers im Jazz vertraut zu machen. Der Band enthält einen Ragtime und eine Bossa Nova, die in geraden Achtelnoten notiert sind, und einen Blues, eine Ballade, eine zweistimmige Invention und einen Jazzwalzer, die in „Swing–Achteln" notiert sind.

Die Verwendung von „Swing–Achteln" wird durch den Hinweis: $\sqcap\!\sqcap = \overset{\ulcorner 3 \urcorner}{\ \rfloor\ \rfloor}$

angezeigt, der sich auf alle in diesen Stücken enthaltenen Achtelbewegungen bezieht, einschließlich der Pausen. Es empfiehlt sich, diese Rhythmen zu üben, bevor man die Stücke in Angriff nimmt.

CONTENTS

❶

BLUES IN TWO

MIKE CORNICK

Universal Edition UE 16 550

RAGTIME

MIKE CORNICK

❸

TWO-PART INVENTION

MIKE CORNICK

❹

BOSSA NOVA

Moderate bossa-nova tempo (♩ = 132)

MIKE CORNICK

(even ♪♪)

⑤

WALTZ FOR MICHAEL

MIKE CORNICK

BALLAD